The Fabian Society

The Fabian Society is Britain's oldest political think tank. Since 1884 the Society has played a central role in developing political ideas and public policy on the left.

Through a wide range of publications and events the Society influences political and public thinking, but also provides a space for broad and open-minded debate, drawing on an unrivalled external network and its own expert research and analysis.

The Society is alone among think tanks in being a democratically-constituted membership organisation, with almost 7,000 members. During its history the membership has included many of the key thinkers on the British left and every Labour Prime Minister. Today it counts over 200 parliamentarians in its number. Member-led activity includes 70 local Fabian societies, the Scottish and Welsh Fabians, the Fabian Women's Network and the Young Fabians, which is itself the leading organisation on the left for young people to debate and influence political ideas.

The Society was one of the original founders of the Labour Party and is constitutionally affiliated to the party. It is however editorially, organisationally and financially independent and works with a wide range of partners of all political persuasions and none.

www.fabians.org.uk.

Joining the Fabians is easy
For more information about joining the Fabian Society and to learn more about our recent publications, please turn to the final page.

TOGETHER

A vision of whole person care for a 21st century
health and care service

Edited by Andy Burnham MP

Fabian Society
11 Dartmouth Street
London SW1H 9BN
www.fabians.org.uk

Head of Editorial: Ed Wallis
Editorial Assistant: Sofie Jenkinson

First published 2013
ISBN 978 0 7163 4119 2

Printed and bound by DG3

British Library Cataloguing in Publication data.
A catalogue record for this book is available from the
British Library.

CONTENTS

CONTRIBUTORS

Caroline Abrahams is director of external affairs at Age UK

Joan Bakewell is a broadcaster, writer and Labour peer. Between 2008 and 2010 she acted as a voice of older people

Andy Burnham MP is shadow secretary of state for health

Alastair Campbell is an ambassador for Time to Change and the author of two books on mental health, *All in the Mind* and *The Happy Depressive*

Angela Coulter is director of global initiatives at the Foundation for Informed Medical Decision Making, Boston, and senior research scientist at the Department of Public Health, University of Oxford

Clare Gerada is chair of the Royal College of General Practitioners

Richard Hawkes is chief executive of Scope

Karen Jennings is assistant general secretary of Unison

James Lloyd is director of the Strategic Society Centre

Michelle Mitchell is charity director of Age UK

Sir Michael Rawlins is former chair of the National Institute for Health and Care Excellence (NICE)

Mary Riddell is a columnist for the *Daily Telegraph*

Gabriel Scally is a public health doctor and professor of Public Health & Planning at the University of the West of England

FOREWORD

Joan Bakewell

She is in her mid 70s and suffering from relatively early dementia: let's call her Miriam. Miriam lived on her own and was coping pretty well. The local social services began to send a series of carers round twice a day but the arrangement proved unsatisfactory. The rota of carers changed from week to week: not ideal for onset dementia. The carers themselves seemed to be ill-trained and overworked, rushing in a for as little as 10 minutes at a time to serve up some inappropriate food (fish and chips for breakfast?) and dash on to their next client. They didn't have time to offer any kind of friendship. They were part of a system that wasn't fit for purpose and, sensing it wasn't being well run, took a casual view of their own responsibilities.

Things had to change: a generous neighbour's family stepped in and took over caring for Miriam. Things improved and Miriam was visibly happier. Then she fell and broke her hip. This time she had to go to hospital where she received fine medical treatment but was kept there for several weeks until she was able to cope once again. The sympathetic neighbours went to visit. They were horrified by what they found. Miriam was, on every occasion, sitting wet and unchanged in a soiled bed. Although able to use the toilet at home, she was not being taken to the ward toilet or allowed to get there by herself. Her mood was depressed and depressing. The visiting neighbours complained but could see that the staff were too over-stretched and overworked to have the time to deliver the standard of care they wanted to provide.

Eventually Miriam came home and has recovered some of her spirit and most of her independence. The kind neighbours keep a close eye on her.

We are all familiar with stories like this, happening both in people's homes and in hospital wards. No outright cruelty is being inflicted. Instead there's a steady erosion of care, and with it human dignity, that sees people spiral downhill in health and wellbeing. This is what awaits each of us and each of those we love unless something is done.

Things must change soon and radically. Andy Burnham understands this and has gone back to the roots of the problem to seek new solutions. And he starts where you need to start, with the individual. What would each of us wish for ourselves if the system was being invented today? The answer is simplistically obvious: we would like all our needs taken care of. Whether they are medical, mental or social, we would just like to feel that the system – whatever system it is – offers us a single service that meets all our needs.

Is that too much to ask? Well, only by asking and being heard can you begin to formulate the answer. And that is the invitation that Andy Burnham set out in his speech given at the King's Fund in January. In it he invites us to think from first principles, to set aside the toppling dinosaur that is the NHS and to consider a fully integrated health and social care system, one that allows people to stay in their homes for as long as possible, supports their welfare and sustains their wellbeing, rather than taking them into hospital where they occupy expensive beds and lose their individuality and sometimes the will to live. It is a bold vision.

Ever since I was asked to be the voice of older people for the last government I have been well aware that caring for people at home is the most effective option. Care in the home calls for a revised culture of caring that draws from the very best people have to offer. It makes each one of them independently responsible for how they deliver the service. This will require a high degree of personal training, rather as Florence Nightingale instilled the ethics of caring into her nurses. The training will focus on a sense of dedication such as we have seen slip away from many of the institutions we turn to for help. This has happened not because people are callous or indifferent, but because the system has been set up to elevate the wrong values. It was certainly important to get waiting times – in hospitals and doctors surgeries – down. And this was done. It was certainly important to make operations available as when they were needed. And this was done. But to make such delivery possible, in some places the culture of box-ticking and clock-watching perhaps became too dominant. Now we need to recover what has been lost.

My stories come from the old who write to me with their concerns. But the same principle of integrated care should work throughout our lives: maternity care, mental wellbeing, hospital stays. The concept of a single integrated service makes sense in many ways – political, financial, social. It is how we might have conceived it had we been able to foresee the range of needs and the scope of medical developments in those euphoric early days of the NHS. Now, with whole person care, we have a chance to re-configure the entire system in a way that makes sense for today's users and suppliers.

INTRODUCTION

Andy Burnham MP

I will never forget the dispiriting journey of my grand-
mother through England's health and care system and
the battles my mum fought to get her basic levels of
care. Like generations of pensioners, my gran lost her
life savings to help fund her care. And like many others,
while there were some lovely people, the standard of care
she received was, at times, poor. She regularly had things
stolen and faced a daily struggle to get the help and care
she needed.

The truth is we currently have a malnourished, mini-
mum-wage social care business that will never provide
the standards of care that we all want for our parents and
for others. It is why many older people end up in hospital, because the quality of care and support they need to
enable them to live at home for longer is, too often, simply
not available.

Stories of older people neglected or abused in care
homes, isolated in their own homes or lost in acute hospitals – disorientated and dehydrated – recur with ever
greater frequency. Baroness Joan Bakewell highlights some
of these issues in her foreword, describing it as a "steady
erosion of care, and with it human dignity".

I've thought long and hard about why this is happening. It is in part explained by regulatory failures and there
are plenty of lessons to be learnt from the failings at Mid-

Staffordshire, Morecambe Bay and Winterbourne View. Changes in nursing and professional practice may also have played a part. But it's not that nurses, or social care workers, don't care anymore. On the whole, the staff who looked after my gran did a magnificent job. It is more that the system is not geared up to deal with the complexities of the ageing society.

Now there are ever greater numbers of very frail people in their 80s and 90s, with intensive physical, mental and social care needs. Hospitals are still operating on a 20th century production-line model, with a tendency to see the immediate problem – the broken hip, the stroke – but not the whole person behind it. As Caroline Abrahams and Michelle Mitchell put it in this collection: "The problem is that most older people have a number of different needs with which they require help but our health system typically responds to each medical condition separately." Hospitals are geared up to meet physical needs, but not to provide the mental or social care that we will all need in the later stages of life. Our hospitals, designed for the last century, are in danger of being overwhelmed by the demographic challenges of this century.

That is the crux of our problem. But to understand its roots, it helps to go back to the 1948 World Health Organisation definition of health: "a state of complete physical, mental and social wellbeing and not merely the absence of disease or infirmity." For all its strengths, the NHS was not set up to achieve this simple vision. It went two thirds of the way, although mental health was not given proper priority, but the third – social – was left out altogether. The trouble is that the 'social' is often the preventative part. Helping people with daily living, staying active and independent, delays the day they need more expensive physical and mental support.

For 65 years, England has tried to meet one person's needs not through two but three services: physical, through the mainstream NHS; mental, through a detached system on the fringes of the NHS; and social, through a means-tested and charged-for council service, that varies greatly from one area to the next. For most of the 20th century, we just about managed to make it work for most people. Now, in the century of the ageing society, the gaps between our three services are getting dangerous.

Wherever people are in this disjointed system, some or all of one person's needs will be left unmet. In the acute hospital ward, social and mental needs can be neglected. This explains why older people often go downhill quickly on admission to hospital. In some places, such is the low standard of social care provision in both the home and care homes, barely any needs are properly met. And in mental health care settings, people can have their physical health overlooked, in part explaining why those with serious mental health problems die 15 years younger than the rest of the population. As Alastair Campbell writes in chapter 3, "This disparity is absolutely unacceptable", and our current approach is "brutally wrong".

This government's response of greater competition and privatisation is the wrong answer. First of all, evidence shows that market-based health systems cost more. International comparisons of the G20 by the Commonwealth Fund show that countries with market-based systems spend a higher proportion of GDP than the UK, as set out in Mary Riddell's chapter.

Secondly, the government's market framework will create more fragmentation with larger numbers of providers and less collaboration – but the future demands integration. Angela Coulter's chapter addresses this point directly. She writes, "what's needed is a shift away from a reactive, disease-focused, fragmented model of care, towards one that is more proactive, holistic and preventative."

On a practical level, families are looking for things from the current system that it just isn't able to provide. They desperately want co-ordination of care – a single point of contact for all of one's needs – but it's unlikely to be on offer in a three-service world. So people continue to face the frustration of telling the same story over again to all of the different council and NHS professionals who come through the door. Carers get ground down by the battle to get support, spending days on the phone being passed from pillar to post.

What is too often missing from the media debate is the effect that our separate health and care systems have on younger people and working-age disabled people. The lack of a whole-person approach holds equally true for the start of life and adults with disabilities. As Richard Hawkes writes in chapter seven, "the care crisis is as real for them as older people." Richard's chapter on "bringing the person back in" rightly calls for social care reform to have "the needs of disabled people at its heart."

If we leave things as they are, people will continue to feel the frustration of dealing with services which don't provide what they really need, that don't see the whole person.

Whole person care

Whole person care is based on two unshakable assumptions. First, that the health and care we want will need to be delivered in a tighter fiscal climate for the foreseeable future, so we have to think even more fundamentally about getting better results for people and families from what we already have. Second, the NHS has no capacity for further top-down reorganisation, having been ground down by the current round. Karen Jennings writes in chapter eight, "There needs to be consideration of how best to change the system while avoiding further unnecessary upheaval for staff and service users." And so I am clear that any changes must be delivered through the organisations and structures we inherit in 2015.

That doesn't mean planning for no change. I am clear that we could get much better results for people, and much more for the £104 billion we spend on the NHS and the £15bn on social care, but only if we take a new approach.

A service that starts with what people want – to stay comfortable at home – and is built around them. If the NHS was commissioned to provide whole person care in all settings – physical, mental, social from home to hospital – a decisive shift could be made towards prevention.

We need incentives in the right place – keeping people healthy at home and avoiding unnecessary hospital admissions. And we must take away the debates between different parts of the public sector, where the NHS won't invest if councils reap the benefit and vice versa, that are utterly meaningless to the public. This is why Labour is asking if the time has come for the full integration of health and social care – one budget, one service, co-ordinating all of one person's needs: physical, mental and social. That would be true human progress in the century of the ageing society. A National Health and Care Service for the 21st century.

The challenges of the 21st century are such that we need to make a shift to commissioning for good population health, making the link with housing, planning, employment, leisure and education. As Clare Gerada argues in chapter ten, "Patients have multiple needs that require more than 'health' and are not best served by competition but instead collaboration between health (physical and mental) services, local government, housing, education and others." This approach to commissioning, particularly in the early years, begins to make a reality of the Marmot vision, where all the determinants of health are in play. Improving public health will not be a fringe pursuit for councils but central to everything that they do. In chapter five, former director of public health, Gabriel Scally sets out how public health can assume a broader role at a local level.

This approach also solves a problem that is becoming increasingly urgent. Councils are warning that, within a decade, they will be overwhelmed by the costs of care if nothing changes. One of the great strengths of the one-budget, whole-person approach would be to break this downward spiral. It would help to give local government a positive future and local communities a real say. The challenge becomes not how to patch two conflicting worlds together but how to make the most of a single budget.

To address fears that health money would be siphoned off into other, unrelated areas, reassurance would need to be provided by a much more clearly defined national entitlement, based around a strengthened National Institute for Health and Care Excellence (NICE). It won't be the job of people at local level to decide what should be provided, but it will be the local job to decide how these entitlements should be provided. Sir Michael Rawlins suggests some possible principles in chapter nine that could underpin such entitlements and what the implications might be for individuals and families should we accept these principles.

The post-war welfare state was created to vanquish the five giants of the 20th century – squalor, ignorance, want, idleness and disease. If we leave things as they are, the 21st century will add a sixth – fear of old age.

Conclusion

If we do nothing, the fear of old age will only grow as we hear more and more stories of older people failed by a system that is simply not geared up to meet their needs. Whole person care means giving all people freedom from this fear, all families peace of mind.

Labour's policy consultation is asking for views on how we pay for social care, with two basic choices – a voluntary or 'all-in' approach. James Lloyd sets out some important issues in debates about these options in his chapter on the future funding and organisation of care.

Whole person care is a vision for a truly integrated service, not just battling disease and infirmity, but able to aspire to give all people a complete state of physical, mental and social wellbeing. A people-centred service which starts with people's lives, their hopes and dreams, and builds out from there, strengthening the NHS in the 21st century. A service which affords everyone's parents the dignity and respect we would want for our own.

I don't yet have all the answers and there is still much debate to be had.

■ How will whole person care provide for the whole child, the whole disabled adult and the whole older person?

■ What will be the role of national and local government?

■ How do we stop the postcode lottery and set out the health and care entitlements that every citizen can expect?

■ How do we pay for social care when resources are tight, with an ageing population?

■ And how can we stop people fearing old age and have true peace of mind throughout a longer life?

These are huge questions that require scale and a sense of ambition in our answers. This book starts to explore some of these challenges and discuss potential solutions. I'm grateful to all the authors of this pamphlet who have all made valuable contributions to Labour's health policy review. Whilst the views expressed in these chapters don't necessarily reflect Labour policy or thinking, the ideas expressed form an important part of the debate. It's a debate that is now urgently needed.

To rise to it we will need political courage and ideas that are equal to the scale of the challenge the 21st century is bringing.

1 | THE POLITICS OF WHOLE PERSON CARE

Mary Riddell

If the economy will dominate the 2015 election, health is likely to be the second most vital issue. With the UK population over 65 set to triple by 2074, Labour stands obliged, in the least propitious of climates, to create a health and care service fit for this century. The question now is how far down the 'whole person care' route the party is prepared to go.

S tart in A&E. Many patients do. By the spring of 2013, pressure on accident and emergency departments was "out of control" and "unsustainable", in the words of the NHS regulator. The Care Quality Commission was not a lone voice. Doctors in the west Midlands wrote to a national newspaper complaining of "toxic over-crowding" and saying that they could no longer guarantee safe care. Another senior clinician declared casualty units "a war zone."

Just over 70 years since Aneurin Bevan, the founder of the National Health Service, decreed that the sound of a dropped bedpan would reverberate through Whitehall, a different echo was percolating from hospital corridors to the Palace of Westminster. The noise in question was the sound of panic, and it was not confined to A&E. Britain's emergency rooms, the focus of the latest crisis in the NHS, were the blown fuse in a dangerously overloaded circuit.

Health always features heavily in election campaigns. The famous poster in the Clinton war room bearing the slogan, "The economy, stupid", carried the less well-remembered subtext: "And don't forget healthcare." By midway through this parliament, it seemed likely that, in a 2015 election dominated by the economy, health would be the second most vital issue.

Ostensibly that is ominous news for David Cameron, who staked his modernising credentials on being the champion and protector of the NHS. Instead, the restructure orchestrated by the first coalition health secretary, Andrew Lansley, at a cost of £3bn, had exacerbated rather than solved the problems that were always going to afflict the service.

By 2013, a health service designed to cure acute patients during their relatively brief lives was instead acting as a warehouse for elderly and chronically sick victims of the war against austerity. One survey showed that £2.7bn, or the equivalent of 20 per cent of care budgets, had been stripped out of adult social care services since 2010. With demand continuing to rise, people who could not get care at home ended up in hospitals, where one in four patients suffers from dementia.

In an age of ageing and of dwindling local government funding, the NHS budget was also under unprecedented pressure. The coalition promise to ringfence health spending, which stood at more than £100bn a year, meant that expenditure until 2015 would remain flat. Apart from a brief period in the 1950s, the NHS has averaged real terms increases of four per cent a year since its establishment, rising to an annual seven per cent since 2000.

In order to maintain quality and standards, the government committed the service to finding £20bn in productivity savings, or at least four per cent a year, by the end of the parliament. The so-called 'Nicholson challenge', named after Sir David Nicholson, the CEO of NHS England, was also unprecedented in NHS history. In the event, the challenge of holding on to his own job proved too much for Nicholson, who announced his resignation in May 2013 after sustained media criticism about his role in the mid-Staffordshire hospital scandal involving patients who died after grossly substandard care. While his target looked set to outlive his tenure, it was increasingly unclear whether the NHS itself could survive such radical surgery.

Successive scandals suggested that in both transactional and emotional terms, the NHS was failing. In November 2010, a Commonwealth Fund survey of 11 leading nations showed that people in the UK had the highest levels of confidence in the effectiveness and affordability of health treatment. A satisfaction level of around 70 per cent had sunk to 58 per cent by 2011, and the signs were that it would fall much lower. Such a slump in public faith might be political cyanide for the Tories, but the decline of the NHS also presaged trouble for Labour in 2015.

Where fiscal policy is arid and impersonal, healthcare speaks to the character of potential governments and their link to the people. Joy over a newborn child or the anguish of a parent's decline bind the governing to the governed. As politicians have long recognised, there is no issue more visceral and more vital than a decent health care system. Thus, when Lord Winston shredded Tony Blair's record in 2000, saying that Britain's stuttering health service was "not as good as Poland's", Blair reacted instantly. Soon after the publication of Lord Winston's interview, the PM was on television announcing billions for the NHS and a plan to achieve spending parity with richer European countries.

Blair's bonanza, bankrolled by the financial upswing after his spell of matching Tory spending cuts, halted the decay. Hospital waiting times fell, as did smoking rates, infant mortality and infections such as MRSA. But even in the good years, and despite all Labour's technocratic reforms and marketisation, the NHS was incubating its own nemesis. Medical advances, shifting patterns of disease, an atomised society and a rapidly ageing population would have produced many challenges, even in an era of plenty. By the time the coalition came to power in 2010, science, demographics and the NHS were conspiring to kill the NHS.

The question for Ed Miliband is just how radical he would dare to be in seeking to salvage the health service. While Labour lagged stubbornly behind the government on economic credibility, the party's polling showed very substantial leads over the Tories on health. Were Labour to win in 2015, that trust would have to be vindicated.

On the question of how best to do it, Labour has been divided. One powerful strand of opinion held that, since Labour is seen as the party of the NHS, the leadership should play up its commitment to the service while avoiding any more risky and expensive overhauls. The second school believed that, without a major consolidation of health and social care, and more money, the current system would founder under the strain.

Andy Burnham, the shadow health secretary, had attempted to make that argument in the last months of the Brown government, when he proposed an estate tax of a flat 10 per cent to fund social care. The cabinet was split down the middle, with half (including many front bench women) backing Burnham and the rest opposed because of the difficulty in selling the policy and because the planned erosion of the popular attendance allowance would play badly among their constituents. As cross-party talks broke down and the Tories inveighed against a 'death tax', Brown abandoned the idea.

By midway through the coalition term, Burnham had revived and refined his masterplan. To the dismay of some colleagues, he told a shadow cabinet meeting that he was about to open consultations on 'whole person care' in which health and social care would be combined in one seamless service. Money would be saved by keeping the elderly out of hospital – a shift that implied the politically risky step of supporting hospital closures.

Rationalisation alone, as Burnham knew, would not be sufficient to pay for reviving social care. With the 800,000 people estimated in 2010 by the King's Fund to have some unmet need, more money would have to be raised either by voluntary contributions (never a reliable method, given people's unwillingness to pay for social insurance) or by an 'all-in' solution, involving either the 10 per cent tax on all estates that Burnham had mooted in the last Labour government or some other compulsory levy on older people.

Despite initial resistance from some colleagues, Burnham got approval for a speech, delivered to the King's Fund in January 2013, in which he exhorted Labour to "rethink its health and care policy from first principles" and announced a consultation that would lead to a service fitting the demands of the 21st century.

The question for Labour now is how far down the Burnham route it is prepared to go. The idea that health and social care must be integrated has consensus across the political spectrum. Stephen Dorrell, the Tory chairman of the health select committee, had made the case for integration long before Burnham's proposal to meld "physical, mental and social care" gained the blessing of the Labour leadership.

Raising a tax to fund better social care is more controversial by far, especially in a climate where all Labour spending plans will be held up to minute scrutiny. Ed Balls's speech, in June 2013, in which he formally embraced the need for austerity as a result of coalition mishandling of the economy, set strict parameters. In a subsequent television interview, Balls styled himself a future chancellor "who would say no" to colleagues.

A leadership anxious to distance itself from the charge that it would embark on a tax-and-spend regime would have to weigh up the risks of another 'death tax' furore, as well as the dangers of embarking on one more structural upheaval to the NHS.

On the second point, Labour would have to show how it could get local and central government to work together without vast bureaucratic changes. On the first, it would have to get its plans out early, sell them properly to the public well before the election and trust that the evident decline in social care would persuade voters – Tories included – that the status quo was unsustainable.

Weighed against the danger of pursuing a durable funding solution is the greater hazard of allowing the current pressures to build. A major crisis would be catastrophic for an incoming Labour government that had promised to protect the health service. In the absence of a firm policy, Labour is poised between the Scylla of a new tax and the Charybdis of an NHS in inexorable decline and a social care system that no longer merits the name. However Labour decides to pay for social care, the current NHS funding ringfence is likely to become unsustainable, since starving local government of money while protecting the NHS budget results in neglect of elderly people and a financial millstone for the health service.

The problems foreseen by Burnham during Labour's last months in power have grown worse and the remedies proposed by the current government inadequate. The latest of many reports on social care, by the economist Andrew Dilnot, proposed a £35,000 cap on the lifetime costs of care, a relaxation of the rule that anyone with savings of more than £23,250 got no help from the state and a voluntary insurance scheme. After many delays, the reforms were finally adopted, in watered-down form, by the coalition, which raised the means-test threshold to £123,000 and set a lifetime cap of £72,000.

The remains of the cross-party consensus around Dilnot foundered in May 2013 when the shadow care minister, Liz Kendall, denounced the government's social care bill ensuring that older people do not have to sell their homes as "a con trick".

As Kendall pointed out, most elderly people in care homes would die before they reached a £72,000 cap, which applied only to care at council rates. By 2016, when the cap takes effect, local authorities would pay around £500 a week for residential care and 'hotel costs' (food and accommodation). With those costs limited to £240, the allowance for social care would be £260. Any individual paying his or her own bills would take about five years to reach the cap – and residents die, on average, after stays of half that length.

Moreover, the 12,500 people who fund their own care and pay up to £140 more a week would have to fund the extra payments themselves, before and after the cap was reached. Some analysts shared Kendall's pessimism, warning that it was extremely unlikely that the cap would result, as hoped, in a developing market for social insurance. Such forecasts should also serve as a warning to Labour that the voluntary insurance idea on which it is also consulting would not work either.

The Tories must hope, as 2015 approaches, that social care has not become so poor a service that it proves impossible to sell their flawed solution to the electorate. Equally, they must rely on the NHS not collapsing under the strain of overload or scandal or both.

Labour, for its part, will have to decide soon whether it will embrace Burnham's 'all-in' solution and use it as the big idea for 2015, the centrepiece of a manifesto and the foundation stone of an Ed Miliband legacy. The alternative is a Burnham-lite variant, in which money is siphoned from health to social care. Although a more rational disposition of resources would alleviate some problems, the expanding black hole of unmet need makes it inevitable that a more drastic answer will be needed.

The shadow health team is developing some innovative ideas, such as a database in which patient information can be shared between all relevant agencies; and public health solutions like the smart phone apps developed in the US by Kaiser Permanente, which allow citizens to plan their diet and exercise, book medical appointments and order prescriptions on line.

Such solutions, necessary as they are, will not solve the challenge of demographics and demand. With the UK population over 65 set to triple to 15.5 million by 2074, and with dementia rife, Labour stands obliged, in the least propitious of climates, to create a health and care service fit for this century. Putting off hard decisions until the economy recovers would, in all likelihood, deal a mortal blow not only to the NHS but to many sick and elderly people thrown on its variable mercy.

2 | THE FUTURE FUNDING AND ORGANISATION OF SOCIAL CARE

James Lloyd

The core vision of whole person care poses fundamental questions about how social care is organised and, crucially in the context of spiralling costs and tight finances, how it is funded. One approach to creating a more generous system of care and support would be a 'something for something' offer with the public, in which new, fair contributions by older cohorts would be explicitly linked to new forms of entitlement and services.

The whole person care challenge raises an important set of questions, and perhaps none more so than for the future organisation and funding of social care. Currently, the UK continues to operate a fundamental divide between the delivery and funding of health and care by the state. Following the Health and Social Care Act (2012), NHS budgets are being devolved to a local level in order for 'clinical commissioning groups' (CCGs) to commission health services from a range of public, private and charitable providers. However, for the public, 'NHS healthcare' will remain free at the point of use. In contrast, public funding for care and support to individuals across the UK is the responsibility of local authorities and characterised by high levels of variation and discretion.

Across the UK, local authorities determine how much support they will provide to individuals through an assessment of their need, taking account of a person's level of disability, as well as the availability of unpaid care from family members. In England and Wales, local authority funding for care is also means tested, with financial support available proportional to a person's income and wealth. In Scotland, public support is not means tested, although in practice this has seen many individuals in residential care continuing to make substantial 'co-payments' toward their care costs, in addition to the 'means blind' contribution from their council.

More recently, after years of lobbying for reform by campaigners, the coalition government has come forward with proposals in response to the recommendations of the Dilnot Commission on the Funding of Care and Support for a new partnership between individuals and the state in paying for care in England. The coalition parties are proposing, from 2016, implementation of the so-called 'capped cost' model, which has three core components. First, a cap of £72,000 – uprated annually with inflation – on the amount an individual will have to contribute to their own care, to protect them from unlimited costs. Second, a new £118,000 'upper capital limit', uprated with inflation, in the means test applied by councils for determining eligibility to financial support for residential care costs. Third, individuals will be expected to make a standardised 'living cost contribution' to residential care costs of around £230 per week when councils work out how much financial support they will provide.

Despite the breadth of the Dilnot Commission proposals, it is widely acknowledged that the vast majority of individuals will have to go on making 'top-up' contributions toward their care costs in residential care, even having reached the 'cap'. Among those local authorities with low benchmark rates for what they will pay for residential care, such as £330 per week in Wigan, individuals will be in residential care for many years before they reach the 'cap'.

Implementing the 'capped cost' reforms will impose extra costs on councils, and by extension, the exchequer. To meet these costs, the coalition government stated in its 2013 budget that the most "fair and simple way" to fund the reforms is to freeze inheritance tax thresholds, as well as to divert to the care system savings resulting from the transition to a single-tier state pension from 2016.

What would whole person care mean for social care and reform of social care funding?

The core vision of whole person care – single health and care budgets funding services from integrated providers able to meet the full diversity of a person's needs – poses fundamental questions: what will be defined as a 'social care need', what forms of support will be defined as 'social care services', and what will be defined as 'social care costs'?

While it may still be possible to recognise some tasks performed for individuals – help with getting out of bed, washing and bathing – as personal care tasks, under some models of whole person care the provision of such support may become inseparable from health care services, and without a clear definition, the costs of such support may be difficult to delineate within single commissioner or provider budgets.

Such 'blurring' around the provision of personal care is nothing new. The interaction between NHS funded continuing care and council-funded care and support has long been a source of confusion and legal dispute.

More pertinently, residential care providers have long pointed out that the 'hotel' aspects of residential care services are inseparable from the personal care aspects, and it is impossible for providers to distinguish 'care' versus 'hotel' costs. For example, a care home worker may walk into someone's room with a cup of tea and find them struggling to put their socks on. By putting down the tea to help with the socks before handing the tea over, the care home worker crosses the 'care' and 'hotel' boundaries in the space of one minute.

Such blurring of services and budgets will be inescapable in realising whole person care if single organisations are commissioned to achieve a broad set of outcomes for services users, including services that once would have been regarded as 'care' and others as 'health', with all the potential for efficiency savings and a cohesive, 'joined-up' experience for service users that this enables.

However, in the context of the current means-tested social care system, this aspect of whole person care poses some profound questions: if social care needs, services and the costs of these services become increasingly blurred, what then should individuals be expected to contribute to the costs of meeting their social care needs?

What would individuals have to pay toward social care under whole person care?

In this context, there are two basic approaches that could be taken to realising whole person care:

- Retain some form of means testing and charging as a contribution from individuals toward their care costs, as a form of 'partnership' between individuals and the state in paying for care;

- An 'all-in' approach in which all public funding for health and care services is provided on a 'means blind' basis, and existing means-testing structures for social care in England are dismantled.

If means testing and private contributions for care costs were retained under whole person care, this will require a definition of what services are free and what services are charged for, the structure of the means-testing framework, and what it is fair to expect individuals to contribute, given that social care services and costs will be increasingly blurred with other budgets and services.

In particular, given the likely blurring of the boundaries around social care needs, services and costs described above, the existing framework that local authorities use to determine eligibility for support – 'Fair Access to Care Services' – as well as the 'Resource Allocation Systems' councils use to fix a financial value of the support individuals need, would all have to be reworked from the ground up. In this scenario, to avoid some services traditionally regarded as health being means tested and charged for, a clear definition of social care services would be required.

Such changes could also require the government to look again at the broader 'partnership' between individuals and the state in paying for long-term care costs, potentially drawing upon the 'capped cost' model, but also other 'partnership' models such as the 2006 'Wanless model' for the state to match-fund what people pay for their care.

Alternatively, an all-in approach to whole person care would scrap all means testing in social care. Entitlement to public funding for care and support would be blind to a person's income and wealth, as the NHS currently is, although services at home would inevitably remain 'carer-sighted' with levels of support provided by the state also taking account of care by family members.

However, even a non-means tested all-in approach will still pose questions around the definition of social care services and cost. This is because of the market in social care services that exists across the UK, and the increasing numbers of individuals who opt to receive their entitlement to local authority support in the form of a cash-based personal budget. Indeed, in practice 'free personal care' would see local authorities give all individuals in residential care a cash-based personal budget as a contribution to residential care costs, set at the level of the council's 'usual cost' rate – the benchmark amount they are willing to pay for a place in residential care. Once in receipt of such a personal budget, those with private means who would currently be 'self-funders' could opt for more expensive care.

Thinking through these complex issues would be part of the challenge to realising whole person care, and could require fundamental changes to the regulation of residential and home care markets, with councils determining 'fair market tariff rates', and defining a basic standard of residential care home that a personal budget will definitely be adequate for.

However, the other key challenge to whole person care is how the exchequer will meet the cost of social care needs across the population in future.

What are the funding options?

Given population ageing, the cost of maintaining the current social care system will grow steadily. The Dilnot Commission estimated that the cost of maintaining current levels of support in 2010 terms in England would increase from £26.2bn in 2010 to £37.7bn by 2025 in 2010 prices, given rising demand owing to demographic change.

The additional cost of the Commission's 'capped cost' reforms was estimated to be equivalent to £1.7bn in 2010 rising to £3.6bn by 2025. The additional cost of free personal care was estimated to be equivalent to £3.8bn in 2010 rising to £7.7bn by 2025. These figures show very clearly that the rising cost of maintaining the current system over the next decade is actually bigger than the additional costs posed by making the system more generous.

What then are the funding options for a more generous system of care and support? Some have argued it would not be fair for the older cohort to put the costs of more generous state support for care costs on to younger people – for example, by putting up working-age income taxes – given the considerable property wealth accrued by many in the older cohort, and the growing challenge for young people to get on the property ladder and pay for higher education.

Some have suggested the options for funding more generous support for care costs under whole person care should centre on potential new contributions from older cohorts, or reconfiguring current entitlements of older people. The coalition government argued in the 2013 budget that inheritance tax is: "a simple and fair way of ensuring that those with the largest estates, who are more likely to benefit from social care reform, help to fund it." Building on George Osborne's argument for using inheritance tax to pay for care, it may be worthwhile exploring whether other configurations of inheritance tax could pay for a more generous care and support system. More broadly, multiple different options exist for older people to contribute to a more generous health and care system from the capital gains on the value of their homes if this was the route that policymakers wished to take.

However, it could also be argued that in the context of population ageing and rising demand, any new approach to the taxation of wealth would be unlikely to provide sufficient resources, and additional 'fiscal levers' would have to be pulled. While controversial, some commentators have flagged options such as introducing national insurance contributions for those working past the state pension age, or restricting eligibility to some other older people's entitlements, such as raising the age at which individuals begin receiving the winter fuel payment.

Clearly, all of these options represent difficult choices. This is why creating a more generous system of care and support could involve a 'something for something' offer with the public, in which new, fair contributions by older cohorts would be explicitly linked to new forms of entitlement and services.

3 | MENTAL HEALTH MATTERS TO ALL OF US

Alastair Campbell

Mental health is still treated completely differently from physical health. To ensure mental health sits at the heart of the whole person agenda, politicians must lead the way in helping to destroy taboos, and underpin changing attitudes by law.

When I think about what the world would look like if mental health were considered of equal value to physical health, I imagine something radically different to what we have now.

I imagine professionals using a recovery-based approach to caring for people with mental health problems, rather than just medicating them and leaving them without proper support or care.

I imagine an end to the postcode lottery of good care, and cultures of restraint replaced by cultures of respect and dignity.

I imagine a time when people are as comfortable talking about their mental health as they are about their physical health. When there is no taboo in asking for help and people are confident in knowing how to look after their own mental health.

I imagine a time when the rights and services that exist for physical health conditions also exist for mental health and we give actual meaning to the legislative reality of parity between the two.

I imagine a time when power is given back to patients, so that they are at the heart of the decision-making process about their care and professionals are responsive to their needs. While this can be a tricky issue when people are in a crisis, that doesn't mean these issues can be avoided. All too often, rights, choice and control go out the window. It doesn't have to be like that. It shouldn't be like that.

I imagine a time when your definition of crisis counts. That the plans you have co-written, along with those who are helping you, determine the care you get. A time when these plans are built with you – not against you.

I imagine a time when doctors and nurses uphold their duty and care and undertake the assessment and monitoring of people's physical health needs, along with recognising and responding to mental health needs. A time when the benefits of peer support are obvious and accepted as of equal value to those of healthcare professionals. A time where people are no more scared to admit to a mental health crisis of the past on their CV than they are a successful fight against cancer.

I imagine a time when we look after the most vulnerable people in our midst, rather than isolating them and leaving them to languish.

I imagine a time when the model of social recovery is the standard, rather than the exception – building in employment support, clinical services, social care, community relationships and carers.

I imagine a time when we are beyond talk of integrating just health and social care services. A time when siloed responses by government agencies in planning services across health, justice, social care, social security and employment are eradicated.

All of these things are at the very heart of 'parity of esteem' – as enshrined in legislation for the very first time in British history in the Mental Health (Discrimination) Act 2013. The legislation is a good step. But if ever we needed an example of the passing of the law being the start, not the end, of the road to progress, this is it. Because for all the progress made, the scale of the challenge – not just in terms of service but also of attitudes – cannot be overestimated

We are a significant way off from the vision I describe. Charities such as Mind and Rethink Mental Illness, and dynamic partnerships like Time To Change, have long been calling for shifts in attitudes, practice and outcomes. Yet as a society, even in the face of gross examples of care and shocking outcomes, we still put up with things that should never be tolerated – in society, in our communities, in our NHS.

The most obvious way to explain what is brutally wrong with our current approach is that despite recent legislation, we treat mental health completely differently from the way we treat physical health. And now with Andy Burnham's whole person care vision we have an opportunity to change that and achieve the 1948 World Health Organisation definition of health: "a state of complete physical, mental and social well-being".

Currently, there are huge waiting times for talking therapies, with no right to access this kind of care, due to technical restrictions with how the National Institute for Health and Care Excellence (NICE) evaluates what it can mandate. The NHS constitution commits to putting mental health on a par with physical health but has a get out of jail free card with regard to those who are being cared for under the Mental Health Act.

There is a lack of crisis and emergency care, at a time when the demands are growing not diminishing. If you show up with a mental healthcare crisis, you are not guaranteed access to care and treatment.

Research into causes, treatment and medication for mental illness are grossly behind the times. Drugs aren't properly evaluated and there is a stranglehold on the amount of investment in mental health research.

When talking about people with mental health problems, the use of poor language continues within the press and politics. We rarely read or hear about schizophrenia unless it is to peddle the myth that the mentally ill are likely to be violent, when in truth they are more likely to be victims of violence than perpetrators. To read some of our papers you would think a good chunk of violent crime is committed by the mentally ill. In fact, fewer than 5 per cent of crimes are committed by people with severe mental illness.

Stigma has a serious impact on the quality of services for people with mental health problems. Too few feel able to complain.

Worst of all are inequalities in rates of premature death. Why do we just accept, as we seem to do, that people with severe mental illness are at risk of dying up to 20 years before the general population? This disparity is absolutely unacceptable. The brutal findings of the independent Schizophrenia Commission, established by Rethink Mental Illness, found that people with severe mental illness are woefully in need of basic levels of physical care and support, despite being at higher risk of preventable illnesses such as diabetes. This is purely in response to the use of anti-psychotics. Yet doctors repeatedly fail to undertake and monitor the most basic of physical needs, such as taking blood pressure, reviewing medication and weighing people.

The crisis care campaign from Mind showed that services are under-resourced, understaffed and overstretched. The reality of the situation is quite stark – four in 10 trusts are failing to meet Department of Health guidance on staff levels. Too often people are turned away. Their calls go unanswered. They are told they are not ill enough to qualify for help. Too few people have care plans, despite being mandated by care regulators.

Mental health has always been a Cinderella service and now it is at further risk. People are asking, what are mental health bodies for? All of this is happening a time when funding for mental health is failing. Faced with the pressure of sweeping reforms to public services, the fear is that without immediate attention things will get much worse before they get better.

The good news is that with a truly integrated, person-centred service, things can and will change, with effort and attention. We used to have an enormous taboo about speaking about cancer. This idea now seems outdated – swept away – and these days no one would ever say that treating cancer was not a priority. You would never ask why someone got cancer. You would never ask why someone has asthma or diabetes. You wouldn't say, 'What have you got to be cancerous about?' 'You shouldn't be having trouble breathing.' You wouldn't leave someone with cancer or lung failure alone to fend for themselves.

Greater openness led to greater political support for tackling cancer. We need to take the same approach to mental illness. We are already seeing – amidst all of the talk of cuts and austerity – that services for people who are experiencing mental illness are being cut.

Where is the outcry that would greet a similar approach to cancer or children's services?

If someone goes to accident and emergency with a broken leg, the hospital is obliged to treat them with courtesy, dignity and responsiveness. If you are faced with the horror of news that you have cancer, the system has to respond within a minimum period of time. But if you are going through a mental health crisis there is no guarantee whatsoever that you will be helped.

Things are improving, but far too slowly for those who are suffering, neglected, isolated and without support or care. One day we will look back and wonder – did we really believe that depression was a lifestyle choice? Did we really believe that if you have been diagnosed with schizo-phrenia you are likely to be violent? Did we really find it acceptable that if you have had a bout of mental illness, you must under no circumstances tell your employer?

Some day we will look back on all of this and despair that we waited so long to right such fundamental wrongs. Change only comes if people make it happen. So where do we begin?

First, with the acceptance that mental health matters to all of us. The way we behave in wider society sets the tone – and government and politicians have a key role to play in helping to destroy taboos and break down barriers. But changing attitudes must be underpinned by law, creating equivalent rights for mental healthcare in the same way as for physical healthcare. People should feel they can be open about their problems.

We need to invest in care, or at the very least, stop cutting services which were always underfunded and straining at the seams. Mental health budgets have reduced in real terms and cuts are having a very real impact. Suicide rates are very worrisome, compulsory treatment is on the rise and the police are systematically detaining people with mental health problems – who have committed no crimes – rather than having to do this only under exceptional circum-stances. The rate of prescriptions of anti-depressants and anti-psychotics continue to rise. We have to turn the tide.

We have to ensure that reforms to health, social care, welfare and public health work for mental health, instead of waiting for our current problems to get worse. Public health professionals urgently need mental health training. GPs must fulfil their basic duty of care.

The most important thing we can do is keep break-ing down barriers in talking about these issues. We must continue to work to end stigma and discrimination – not just with employers, friends, and in our communities, but within the very culture of the NHS.

Politics also has a massive role to play in this. Last year in parliament, for the first time in history we heard four MPs speaking out about their own experiences. They received an overwhelmingly positive response from the public but there is so much more work the political class can do.

We can wait no longer. The time to change is now.

4 | EMPOWERING PATIENTS

Angela Coulter

Patients are the greatest untapped resource in healthcare. Recognising their capacity as assets and co-producers of health does not require further structural change. Instead what's needed is a shift away from a reactive, disease-focused, fragmented model of care, towards one that is more proactive, holistic and preventative, in which people are encouraged to play a central role in managing their own care.

The NHS continues to be a hugely popular public service, despite its much-publicised failings. Disasters, including atrocious care of elderly patients in certain NHS hospitals, and sensationalist tabloid headlines, have done surprisingly little to shake public trust in the service, which remains high. Yet look beyond the headlines and you find signs of a sluggish response to changing patient needs and expectations and a paternalistic culture that prevails in spite of the rhetoric about 'no decisions about us without us'.

Both the current government and the previous one sought to address these problems through promoting 'choice' and 'voice'. Encouraging competition between providers (choice) was used alongside patient feedback (voice) in the hope that this would increase responsiveness, improve efficiency and drive up quality.

Choice of provider

Choice policy views patients as consumers who, if armed with information on the quality of care provided by different organisations (hospital or general practice), will shop around for the best. In theory, since payments follow the choices that patients make in a competitive health-care market, providers should have an incentive to attract them, and the collective act of shopping around should send signals to poor performers to pull their socks up or go under. Fixed national tariffs should ensure that providers compete on quality not price, so quality standards overall should rise. Or so the government hopes.

Critics of this approach claim that it leads to increased privatisation, inefficiencies due to wasteful duplication of services and that it panders to the concerns of a middle-class urban elite, leaving those in less advantaged groups with few options. Barriers to exercising choice of provider might include travel costs, job constraints, communication problems or lower levels of health literacy. And in some remoter areas, the choice of specialist services remains limited or non-existent unless people are willing to travel long distances at their own expense.

More than 10 years after a Labour government first introduced the provider choice policy, it remains difficult to judge whether either its proponents or its critics have been proved right. There is no doubt that the idea of choice is intrinsically attractive to many people. Surveys show that older people, those with lower educational qualifications, and those from non-white or mixed ethnic groups are especially likely to say they value choice.[1] But few are willing to spend much time looking for performance data to inform their choices.[2] There is some evidence that hospitals in regions where there is a greater number of competing providers have performed better in relation to certain quality indicators, but no one has yet demonstrated that this is the result of an increase in informed choices by individual patients.[3]

Greater choice and competition may lead to improved care in certain circumstances, for example shopping around for the best provider of common elective surgical procedures might make sense. But most patients are more interested in having a say in how their condition is treated or managed than in choosing hospitals.[4]

Choice of treatment

There are often many different ways to treat a health problem, each of which may lead to a different set of outcomes. Decisions that can affect people's quality of life in important ways should not be left to doctors alone. In these cases it is important that patients are informed about the potential benefits and harms of each of the options and encouraged to participate in selecting the best treatment for them.

This process, known as shared decision making, involves the provision of reliable, balanced, evidence-based information outlining treatment options, outcomes and uncertainties, together with decision support counselling with a clinician or health coach to clarify options and patients' preferences.

This idea finds favour in many quarters. The Department of Health, the General Medical Council and many other bodies have published statements advocating shared decision making and it is one of several important commitments in the NHS constitution. Yet national patient surveys (a feature of the 'voice' policy) show that many, if not most, patients do not receive sufficient information to make an informed decision about their treatment or care.[5] Clinicians often think they are better at informing and involving patients than they actually are. A very different picture emerges when you ask patients.

It is often assumed that patients who are well-informed about treatment options will choose the most expensive, but in fact the opposite is the case. Well-informed patients tend to be more risk-averse than the clinicians who treat them, often leading to reduced demand for more invasive and expensive procedures when they have access to good information.[6] Making evidence-based patient decision aids available and training clinicians in better risk communication could be a highly cost-effective way to empower patients and encourage evidence-based practice.

Choice of care plan

People with long-term conditions constitute 30 per cent of the total population and account for 70 per cent of health and social care expenditure. They are the heaviest users of hospital care, accounting for 70 per cent of hospital bed use, 64 per cent of outpatient appointments, and about 50 per cent of GP consultations. Improving care for these people is the greatest challenge we face if the NHS is to deliver greater value. This means transforming the service from a system that is largely reactive, responding mainly when a person is sick, to one that is much more proactive and preventative, focused on supporting people's ability to self-manage their health.

People with chronic conditions, those with multiple or complex conditions, including mental health problems, and frail older people nearing the end of life place great value on continuity and on well-coordinated personalised care, delivered by integrated teams of professionals.[7]

Personalised care planning aims to ensure that patients' values and concerns shape the way long-term conditions are managed. Instead of focusing on a standard set of disease management processes determined by clinicians, patients are encouraged to select treatment goals and to work with clinicians to determine their specific needs for treatment and support. In this more collaborative approach, problems are discussed and tackled, including patients' accounts of the practical, social and emotional effects of their condition on their daily lives. Treatment goals are agreed, management and support options are reviewed, and plans are recorded and shared.

It has been government policy in England since 2010 to ensure that all patients with long-term conditions are actively involved in planning their care, but a co-ordinated, personalised approach is not yet the norm in everyday practice.[8] Effective implementation must involve significant organisational and cultural change, plus deter-mined leadership and effective monitoring. The rewards are potentially great. Encouraging anticipatory care and prevention, better support for self-management and better use of community assets, could create significantly greater value at lower cost than is possible with the current network of reactive services. One estimate suggests this policy could produce savings of about £4.4bn per year if properly implemented.[9]

An untapped resource

Patients have been described as the greatest untapped resource in healthcare. Recognising their capacity and that of local communities as assets and co-producers of health, not simply resource-users, could do much to transform the quality and sustainability of the NHS. This type of reform does not require further structural change. Instead what's needed is a shift away from a reactive, disease-focused, fragmented model of care, towards one that is more proactive, holistic and preventative, in which people are encouraged to play a central role in managing their own care.

Policy levers that will be important include:

- Incentives for clinicians and commissioning groups to transform traditional consulting styles

- More integrated team working

- New funding mechanisms and pooled budgets that facilitate co-ordinated care

- New types of training courses for health and social care professionals

- More flexible and less fragmented commissioning with patient and community involvement

- More patient access to electronic records

- Better systems for sharing data across service boundaries

- And co-ordinated metrics for monitoring progress and outcomes

Endnotes

1. Dixon A, Robertson R, Appleby J, Burge P, Devlin N, Magee H. *Patient choice: how patients choose and how providers respond.* London: The King's Fund, 2010.
2. Marshall M, McLoughlin V. *How do patients use information on health providers?* BMJ. 2010;341:c5272.
3. Gaynor M, Moreno-Serra R, Propper C. Can competition improve outcomes in UK health care? Lessons from the past two decades. *Journal of health services research & policy.* 2012 Jan;17:49–54. PubMed PMID: WOS:000300804000007. English.

4. Coulter A. *Do patients want a choice and does it work?* BMJ. 2010;341:c4989.

5. Coulter A, Collins A. *Making shared decision-making a reality.* London: King's Fund, 2011.

6. Stacey D, Bennett CL, Barry MJ, Col NF, Eden KB, Holmes-Rovner M, et al. *Decision aids for people facing health treatment or screening decisions.* Cochrane Database Syst Rev. 2011;10:CD001431. PubMed PMID: 21975733. Epub 2011/10/07. eng.

7. Department of Health. *Long Term Conditions Compendium of Information 2012* 10/11/2012; (Third edition). Available from: http://www.dh.gov.uk/prod_consum_dh/groups/dh_digitalassets/@dh/@en/documents/digitalasset/dh_134486.pdf.

8. Burt J, Roland M, Paddison C, Reeves D, Campbell J, Abel G, et al. Prevalence and benefits of care plans and care planning for people with long-term conditions in England. *Journal of health services research & policy.* 2012 Jan;17 Suppl 1:64–71. PubMed PMID: 22315479. Epub 2012/02/15. eng.

9. Morioka S, Farrington S, Hope P, Brett K. *The Business Case for People Powered Health.* London: NESTA, The Innovation Unit, Private Public Ltd., 2013.

5 | THE PUBLIC HEALTH CHALLENGE

Gabriel Scally

The NHS will be overwhelmed by growing demands for healthcare unless prevention becomes a priority. But improving public health is often long term, leaving the agenda at risk from short-termism and the silo mentality of Whitehall departments. However, there are rock-solid arguments why investment in public health action – from smoking to tackling the housing crisis to creating a new culture of food and drink – will deliver for the public purse.

It was Cicero who wrote '*Salus populi suprema lex esto*': the health of the people should be the supreme law. It would a pretty good slogan for a government that wants to tackle some of the major public health problems that face the population. Dealing effectively with health inequalities, obesity, alcohol abuse and tobacco requires a firm and focussed approach across government if progress is to be made. The balancing of competing interests, many of them driven by the profit motive, while putting the interests of the public first, is a task that only a Labour government seems capable of achieving.

The payback would be enormous. A healthier population means a lower burden on the taxpayer from healthcare costs and sickness benefits and it also means lower costs on business from sickness absence and incapacity. Much more importantly, it gives people happier, longer lives with less impairment through immobility and pain. This isn't something that can be achieved by individual effort; it can only be achieved through the organised efforts of society with leadership and support from across government.

Labour can look back on a record of significant achievement on some major public health issues when they were last in office. Helping hundreds of thousands of people addicted to illegal substances get the treatment they needed through joint action and dedicated funding by the Department of Health and the Home Office did a huge amount to reduce violent and acquisitive crime on our streets. It also improved immeasurably the lives of substance abusers and their families. Cutting teenage pregnancy was also the target of a major cross-government programme. Although it was slow to get going, in the latter years of Labour's time in office, thanks to modest but well-targeted investment in contraceptive services, it did achieve substantial reduction in the pregnancy rate. Similarly, the hugely popular 'healthy schools' programme was enormously effective in getting schools to realise that improving the health of their pupils could be a major contribution to improving educational attainment.

More mixed was the Labour record on tackling the long-standing issues of tobacco and alcohol, as well as the growing problem of obesity. Although there were some legislative achievements on environmental tobacco smoke and promotion of tobacco products, they sometimes appeared to be the acts of a government wary of being accused of promoting a 'nanny state'.

It was the work of the late Derek Wanless that finally, in the latter part of Labour's time in power, looked as if it changed the game. He graphically pointed out that unless we spent much more effort and resources on preventing illness we would be completely unable to afford the growing costs of an obese and ageing population, burdened by the pending epidemic of non-communicable diseases such as diabetes and stroke.

However, government caution about leading sharply focussed action on the root causes of ill-health led to large sums being poured into centrally-driven social marketing campaigns. It is much easier for the Department of Health to run advertisements suggesting to people what they should do, for example take more exercise, than make the cross-government changes in planning policy and infrastructure spend that would make it easier and safer for children to walk and cycle to and from their schools.

Within a few months of the coalition coming into power in 2010 it was clear that they would abolish the National Treatment Agency for Substance Misuse and shut down both the Teenage Pregnancy Unit and the healthy schools programme. The miserable record of the Lib Dems and Tories on public health is well illustrated by their vacillation on standardised packaging of tobacco and minimum pricing of alcohol. Such spinelessness can't be a surprise given their much trumpeted 'responsibility deal' which puts industry interests firmly in the driving seat when it comes to steering government policy in several fields of major public health concern. Even more humiliating for the coalition is the abject failure of their much-vaunted cabinet sub-committee on public health, abolished when ministers from many Whitehall departments ignored it completely and didn't bother attending its meetings.

Lessons learnt

We can learn several valuable lessons for the future from the varying experience of recent governments. Great progress can be made through having a focussed approach, dedicated staff, an adequate and protected budget and a delivery chain that reaches into and supports communities across the country. Where cross-Whitehall commitment and resourcing is put in place it can be very effective, but getting inter-departmental buy-in is not at all easy to achieve. The financial pressures of urgent health-care needs can lead to the neglect of prevention and the siphoning off of funds from public health programmes. It isn't possible to change the health of the population without offending at least some of the vested interests that make profit out of some of the things that make us unhealthy. Spending on social marketing or unevidenced 'screening' programmes is seductive because it gives the instant appearance of doing something, but can be both ineffective (perhaps even damaging) and wasteful of time and resources. Investing in improving health is for the long term; judgements about investment must take that into account.

Building these lessons into a programme for a future government isn't an easy task. The nature of the mission of improving public health is often long term and the benefits are usually gained maximally by future generations. A good example of this is smoking. The incidence of lung cancer in women continues to rise, reflecting smoking patterns in the 60s and 70s rather than today's reduced levels of smoking. It therefore requires a breadth of approach that is perhaps best worked out in opposition so that the framework of what is to be done is broadly agreed in advance. Otherwise short termism and the silo mentality of Whitehall departments may well, yet again, intervene and stymie drive and innovation.

Improving health at a time of austerity

It would be great if, for once since the 19th century, there was to be substantial and consistent investment in the public health system and programmes. But, realistically, public health will not be exempt from the 'laser focused' approach to public spending. But there are rock-solid arguments why investment in public health action will deliver for the public purse.

Smoking, still the biggest public health issue we face, is a case in point. If you want to put money back into the pockets of some of the least well off people in the country, helping them stop smoking is a surefire winner. Only about 20 per cent of the adult population smoke but it isn't evenly distributed in society. More than twice the proportion of people in routine and manual occupations smoke compared to those in professional occupations. If someone who smokes 20 cigarettes a day quits, that is more than £2,500 he or she will have to spend on other things each year. We know that active tobacco control programmes can convince people to quit and that they put millions of pounds a year back into some of our most disadvantaged communities all over the country.

Tackling the housing crisis will undoubtedly be a priority for an incoming Labour government and some elements of the action needed could be tailored jointly with the NHS to help avoid the deaths of more than 200 elderly people every day during the winter months. It isn't just the avoidable deaths. For every death there may be up to eight other hospital admissions with respiratory and cardiovascular problems. Helping people stay in their own home instead of care homes and hospitals should be a central common objective of health and housing policies.

Newly remade cities

The need for more and better quality housing driven by population growth and increased longevity will feed the pace of urbanisation. When we put the recession behind us, the job creation that will be necessary will create a disruptive dynamic in our cities and place a premium on their recasting themselves as places that people want to live and businesses want to develop. Rethinking the way in which people and goods move about in order to enhance mobility and reduce carbon emissions and pollution will give us the opportunity to create healthy, livable cities.

At the present time, our cities are killing us. Not only because of poor housing standards but also through other public health problems such as air pollution. At least 24,000 premature deaths every year are attributable to air pollution. The quality of the air we breathe is of course worse in our cities and up to 70 per cent of that pollution is attributable to road transport. We should be actively remaking our cities as places where modern approaches to walking, cycling and efficient and clean public transport reduce pollution substantially. Modern livable cities would also help us do more about the health of our children. At present 38 per cent of primary school children travel to school by car. Making it safe for every child to walk or cycle to and from school should be a key priority.

A new culture of food and drink

Our system of feeding ourselves is riven with problems from top to bottom. There is a crisis on the land as farming incomes are squeezed by the supermarkets and agribusiness drives further intensification and high carbon input agricultural practices. We have throwbacks to Victorian times as foodbanks and charity are relied upon to feed hundreds of thousands whilst food is wasted elsewhere in enormous quantities. At the consumer end of the supply chain there is a crisis of confidence fuelled both by scandals involving food adulteration and the continued promotion of processed foodstuffs high in fat, salt and sugar. If we are to save ourselves from a tidal wave of obesity and chronic disease such as diabetes then a new relationship between the population and the food we eat must be forged.

Change is possible and should be built on increasing agricultural output in the UK with a concentration on levels of fruit and vegetable production by sustainable means. The shortening of supply chains and support for local food hubs and markets would increase margins for producers and value for consumers. The use of public spending in areas such as the NHS and education sectors to support the use of healthy, locally-produced food would provide security for suppliers and improve what is often a poor food offer to patients, students and staff. Practical education about food should be a priority in schools.

The benefits of helping huge numbers of people by achieving substantial reductions in serious diseases such as cancer and diabetes are far too great to repeat the mistake of thinking that a few expensive television advertisements are going to cure an ailing food culture. The dynamic implementation of an imaginative cross-sector approach is long overdue.

A public health system that can deliver on reducing ill-health and inequality

The NHS will be overwhelmed by growing demands for health care unless prevention becomes a priority for action. The transfer of public health responsibilities to local government is a progressive step, despite the timing of this major change being far from helpful given the huge cuts being made in budgets. But in the future, with a move to whole person care and integrated services, the opportunity will arise for public health to assume a broader role at a local level. The actions of the coalition have, however, weakened what was a world class public health service. There are now many more people working in public health as part of central government than in all the local authorities in England put together. The independent and authoritative regionally-based Public Health Observatories have been abolished and the role of local directors of public health downgraded in many places. The absence of strategies, plans and targets to improve the health of the country is without precedent, as is the absence of a strong public health voice close to the centre of government.

The rebuilding of a system that can protect us from infectious diseases and other hazards as well as providing the drive to tackle the burden of preventable non-communicable disease will be a vital task. The role of non-governmental organisations will be of great importance in this work, alongside the further development of public health understanding and expertise across all parts of civil society.

Conclusion

Much was achieved under the last Labour government in learning what we need to do to reduce the unacceptable burden of early death and chronic disease that falls on our least well-off citizens. Putting into place actions to decisively reduce inequality must be a priority right across government. The prize – helping people live longer, happier, more economically and socially productive lives – is a prize worth having.

6 | TRUE PEACE OF MIND

Caroline Abrahams and Michelle Mitchell

For older people, the technical detail of how services are configured matters much less than that they are properly co-ordinated and are organised around them. Resources must be targeted at helping services to work together across a wide spectrum, including housing and social care, and at measuring performance based on the long-term, sustained wellbeing of older people.

A few lines into his King's Fund speech which launched whole person care, Andy Burnham asked a profound question for us all as individuals and for our country too: "how can we stop people fearing old age and have true peace of mind throughout a longer life?"

Frankly, it is heartbreaking that such a question should even have to be asked. Previous generations would surely tell us that we ought to be viewing the fact of increasing longevity as a gift. Unfortunately though, at present there is a widespread lack of confidence in our health and care system to provide, on a consistent basis, first rate care for the older people who make up an increasing proportion of our population. As a result, Andy Burnham's question seems not only highly pertinent, but also tough to answer with real conviction.

Earlier this year an Age UK survey found that only one in three of the public were confident that an older person would be treated with dignity if they had to go into hospital. After a succession of shocking stories in the media about poor hospital care, culminating in the Francis Report, it is not surprising that public confidence should be so low. But set this against the huge public affection and support for the NHS, and it suggests that something has gone badly wrong in our health and care system, which we must now urgently put right.

As Andy Burnham made clear later on in his speech, a big part of the problem is that our hospitals were designed to meet the needs of the population of this country fifty or more years ago, not the population we have today, let alone the one we will have tomorrow. And what is true most obviously of our hospitals also applies to many other elements of our health and care system too, and perhaps most of all to their capacity – or more frequently their lack of it – to work together seamlessly to offer older people the co-ordinated help they need.

The problem is that most older people have a number of different needs with which they require help but our health system typically responds to each medical condition separately, and our social care system isn't really a 'system' at all. There is not enough social care compared to the scale of the demand, and the quality of what is available is often not good enough.

70 per cent of people over 75 live with a major long-term condition and a quarter live with two or more. For many older people, the impact on their health and wellbeing is not so much the severity of a single condition, but the challenge of living with several and of managing them.

So rather than care being planned in a way that accounts – say – for an older person's chronic chest disease, diabetes and mild dementia together with some social care and housing needs, what is offered is usually piecemeal and segmented, as well as often being inadequate in terms of the response to their social care and housing needs.

This substantially increases the risks of a person's health getting worse and leads to missed opportunities to avoid admissions to hospital. This is also inherently upsetting and frustrating for older people and leaves families and friends often trying to do the joining up between services and professionals that the 'system' is unable to do for itself.

Seen from this perspective it is clear that older people need care that views them as a whole person and that responds to them effectively on that basis. We have to target our efforts and our resources at helping services to work together across a wide spectrum, including housing and social care, as well as all kinds of medical care, and at measuring performance based on the long-term, sustained wellbeing of older people, not just on whether they are able to access a treatment at a particular point in time.

The statistics demonstrate the scale of the challenge we face in transforming our health and care services so they become a genuinely whole system that is fit for purpose tomorrow as well as today. There are 12 million people of state pension age, almost one in five of the UK population, and they comprise the majority of all NHS clients. But as a result of increasing longevity, the number of people aged over 60 is projected to pass 20 million by 2031 and the number of those aged over 85, the group most likely to need care, is projected to double over the next twenty years. A further important consideration is that some 820,000 older people are believed to be suffering from dementia today, but by 2025 the number is expected to exceed a million.

So longevity is with us now, but it is expected to accelerate quite sharply over the next two decades. There is clearly no time to waste in redesigning our health and social care system so it is well placed to respond.

With statistics like these, and on-going, significant pressures on the NHS budget, it would be easy to conclude that the task of transforming our health and care system is beyond us, but at Age UK we believe this is far too fatalistic. In addition, rather than tight finances acting as an impossibly high barrier against change, we think they create an overwhelming case for change.

For example, in 2010–11, more than 200,000 people aged 75 or over were readmitted to hospital within a month of discharge. Older people also experience longer stays in hospital on average too.

Such repeated spells of hospitalisation are often distressing for older people, and rather than supporting their health and wellbeing they can actually undermine it, especially if inertia in arranging extra help at home to support their recovery means they have to stay in hospital for longer than their medical condition really requires.

And these preventable hospital stays are expensive too, with every bed day costing around £250. What a waste of money many of these spells must be, especially as in many cases the risk factors that contribute to them can be effectively managed if the right prevention and early intervention approaches are in place in localities. Good community health care and social care are crucial components and although they are not cost free, they certainly deliver better results than a hospital stay. But such good local provision is at best patchy and at present reduced budgets are often leading to services shrinking, not expanding as would make most economic sense.

Hospitals can be, and should be, very good places for older people. They're just not good places for all older people all of the time. Yet this typifies the way they are often used by local health economies, because there's nothing else and because older people's care is more often episodic rather than a planned and co-managed 'pathway of care'.

Part of the answer is for there to be a greater focus within the NHS on helping older people to manage their own health more effectively at home. This would help to sustain their resilience and enable them to be independent for as long as possible, which is what older people say they want.

At present we are missing some very obvious opportunities to do this: last year Age UK research found that among people aged over 75, four in five of those with diabetes had not received training to self-manage their conditions; almost three in four had not had a discussion with their health care team about preventing their arthritis from getting worse; and four in five of those with a history of falls had not had strength or balance training. Yet interventions like these are simple and low cost, and they would make a huge difference.

There is also growing evidence that older people are often unable to access treatments that are known to be effective and for health issues that disproportionately affect people in later life. A third of breast cancer diagnoses occur in women over 70 yet treatment rates peak at 65 and decline sharply thereafter. Mental health treatments are also far less robust in people over 75, who are six times more likely to be on tranquilisers for common conditions.

This paints a picture of poor management and the storing up of crises, with health and care services intervening most often only when stored up problems spill over into often less successful and more costly urgent and emergency health services.

Another problem is that unfortunately, older people often tell us that they are not treated as an individual and a partner in their own care, and this must change. Older people should be able to expect a thorough assessment of their health and their needs, without misplaced assumptions about their age interfering with diagnosis or treatment plans. Care should be planned and delivered based on what they want out of it, not what their health-care team expects them to get out of it. At present there is little to suggest these things routinely happen for older people accessing health and care services.

In this sense the term 'person-centred care' is a descriptor of the problem, the case for change, and the solution all in one. It describes what is absent, why it is important, and how the NHS and care services need to change how they work.

Would systems still fail to integrate if all outcomes were truly focused solely on the person being treated? It would certainly be much more difficult to justify silos of care and treatment if everything was planned and judged specifically on the impacts on patients and their carers.

By involving people in their care you establish what they want to achieve, you use their expertise about their body and the condition and you better enable them to look after their own health. Older people have told us: "I have an inquisitive mind and I want to be involved. It's my body and I want to be involved in what's being done to me." A whole literature on shared decision-making provides compelling evidence for what working in partnership with patients can achieve when carried out effectively.

So Andy Burnham's vision for whole person care shows that the political debate is moving in the right direction. For older people the technical detail of how services are configured matters much less than that they are properly co-ordinated and are organised around them: to be meaningful, whole person care must be just that, with the (older) person always at the centre.

If we can achieve this we will go a long way towards being able to answer that crucial question Andy Burnham posed in his speech: "how can we stop people fearing old age and have true peace of mind throughout a longer life?" Indeed, this deserves to be one of the key tests of any new health and care policy approach.

7 | BRINGING THE PERSON BACK IN

Richard Hawkes

A third of people using care services are working- age disabled adults, and in many areas they take up half of the local budget. With whole person care, Labour could be on the cusp of creating a care system fit for disabled people in the 21st century. But only if some big questions are answered, not least how a health system free at the point of access can be merged with a care system so dependent on eligibility and assessment.

Disabled people across the country were smiling to themselves as Andy Burnham took the stage and spoke of his vision for 'whole person care'. Smiling because his vision was strong, positive and put disabled people at the heart of health and social care reform. But also because they know how difficult it will be to turn this sentiment into practice.

Burnham's vision is of active people in control of their health and support, collaborating with the state to achieve better outcomes. Seeing people in the round and increasing choice and control are core tenets of the disability and independent living movements. Needing to manage a health condition like MS or diabetes, needing support to wash because you lack manual dexterity, or needing specialist support to communicate with people in your community because you are deafblind should not be limiting, but be the cornerstone of independence. Providing good care and support can enable people to take part in family life, get involved in their local community and go to work.

You'd be forgiven for thinking that the reform of health and social care was only about our ageing society, so frequently are debates only framed as a crisis facing older people. It's true that there are examples of older people being shockingly treated in our NHS, left undignified in care homes and kept in hospital too long because support isn't available in their community. Their care crisis rightly needs to be a national priority, but so does the care crisis facing disabled adults. The care crisis is as real for them as older people, and cases like the neglect and abuse of patients by staff at Winterbourne View need to be a wake-up call to decision makers on the need to focus on disability too.

A third of people using care services are working-age disabled adults, and in many areas they take up half of the local budget. Furthermore, the number of disabled adults needing care and support is increasing. In 2010/2011, 1.1 million disabled people relied on the social care system, but by 2020 we anticipate that the number of people in need of care will have risen to 1.3 million. Traditionally this group may not be regarded with as much electoral attraction as the 'grey vote', but social care reform that does not have the needs of disabled people at its heart is sure to fail.

Care in crisis

The promise of a health and social care system that is tailored around the individual, and responsive to their needs, is more than an alluring prospect for disabled people. Too often the clashes between the two systems leave disabled people distraught, isolated and without adequate support to get out of bed, get washed, cook a warm meal and participate in their local community. Cash-strapped commissioners argue over whether or not a need is the responsibility of the NHS or of social care services – leaving disabled people to fall through the cracks of decisions that are sometimes made with the financial considerations first and foremost.

Chronic underfunding of adult social care has left, on conservative estimates, a £1.2 billion gap in funding that is growing fast. In the last year alone, the number of 18–64-year-olds receiving social care fell by more than 36,000 – a drop of seven per cent. Since 2008 the number of people using care has fallen by at least 90,000, or one in six of all people using care. These people have been left to fend for themselves or tied to the goodwill of friends and family. This is hardly a dignified way to live and falls short of the ambitions we all should have for disabled people to live as full, independent and equal members of our society.

Even when people do get support, the picture is not much better. Councils are still reeling from a 33 per cent cut to their settlement meaning that social care budgets are being tightly squeezed. To paraphrase the outgoing president of the Association of Directors of Adult Social Services (ADASS), Sarah Pickup, social care is not an island, and a cut to council budgets is a real-terms cut to frontline care services. Councils are responding by restricting access to care and putting in place ways of rationing the little resource they have available locally.

Our care system is one that only intervenes when people are in crisis. Without access to adequate social care, disabled adults' needs escalate and their health and wellbeing deteriorates. There is also a significant economic cost: without adequate support, people's needs escalate and many are fated to re-enter the system at a later date, with a far greater level need and at a much higher cost to the state through increased dependency on the NHS, welfare benefits and crisis care services.

The challenges whole person care will have to address

In his speech to the King's Fund Andy Burnham said that this is a 'green paper moment', the start of a new conversation. It's a welcome conversation, but unless it tackles some of the systemic issues disabled people face it will not fulfil the aspirations it is based upon.

There are some crucial questions that the Labour health policy review must address if the 'whole person care' approach is to end the care crisis for working age disabled people:

1. Who is in and who is out?

Disabled people tell us that the most important issue they face is whether or not they are deemed eligible for care and support. Unlike the NHS, adult social care is not free at the point of use and you have to have an eligible level of need to get support. At the moment councils have discretion as to where they set eligibility for adult social care. Because of chronic underfunding successive governments have allowed eligibility across England to rise significantly with 87 per cent of councils setting it at the very highest levels ('substantial' and 'critical' levels).

Although the care bill is set to introduce a much anticipated and welcome national eligibility threshold, there is considerable concern that this threshold will be set at an equivalent to the highest levels. Recent modelling by the Personal Social Services Research Unit at the LSE suggests that on conservative estimates at least 105,000 disabled people will be locked out of the system as a consequence. This will leave them dependent on the grace and good will of family, friends or strangers to help them with intimate tasks like, washing or going to the toilet. It further drives them into crisis.

Fundamental to the idea of whole person care is who is captured in the system. Could we move towards an

integrated system where more people are eligible for preventative support that maximises their independence and
enables them to contribute to their local community?

2. How do we spark a rapid transformation in care?

In 1948, the National Assistance Act established the NHS
and set out new duties on councils to provide accommodation and support to disabled people who needed
assistance. But it was not until 22 years later that disabled
people's rights to social care were strengthened under the
Chronically Sick and Disabled Persons Act of 1970, introduced by the late Lord Morris of Manchester.

Since then, government policy has sought to incremen-
tally improve support social care, with a noticeable cultural
shift from the 1970s culture of institutional care, towards a
system that increases people's choice and control over the
care they receive. Previous Labour strategies did much to
further this agenda, particularly through 'putting people
first' and 'valuing people now', as well as through the
introduction of devolved payments for disabled people
to commission and purchase their own support like direct
payments and personal budgets.

But the legacy of an outmoded care and support system
remains. In England too many disabled people live in
institutional residential care, segregated from their local
community and without a say in how their health is
managed and their care provided. Recent moves to person-
alise care services are welcome and are having a tangible
impact on the lives of disabled people. But there is a long
way to go. Despite many providers wanting to modern-
ise, they struggle to find a truly collaborative approach to
designing a programme of change that engage both disabled people and statutory commissioners.

We don't yet have the modern care market disabled
people want and need to be independent in their communities. Yes – best practice and innovation is out there, but

it is often patchy and, as Scope's report with the new economics foundation demonstrated, vulnerable to further austerity. Disabled people should not have to wait another decade for local markets to catch up with their own aspirations for care and support. So, how can whole person care be a catalyst for change which sparks a new generation of support services?

3. Do markets drive better quality and outcomes?

The drive towards increasing choice and control has resulted in budgets being devolved to disabled people to commission their own services, rather than relying on councils to purchase them on their behalf. For many, the devolution of funding to disabled people was seen as a radical revolution and enables disabled people to actively shape the care and support they receive. However Jenny Morris, in a paper for the Joseph Rowntree Foundation, questions whether marketising people's lives is the most effective way of driving improvement in support services for disabled people.

Managing your own budget does allow for flexibility, particularly if the care you receive provides a continuity of support. But, taking on commissioning responsibility and managing your own staff also mean you become an employer and need to effectively manage your own care budgets. Opinion and experience of this amongst disabled people is split. While some say it is empowering and, for the first time, puts them in control of their life, others say they are bogged down with bureaucracy and administration when what is most important to them is person-centred support, focused on the outcomes they want to achieve.

The political philosopher Michael Sandel challenges us to think about whether markets increase the quality of care and outcomes for individual, or if they corrupt the relationships between people necessary for effective support.

Currently, the assumption is that they are helping to transform social care. A whole person approach to care must investigate the extent to which markets and consumers can drive an improvement in the quality of support disabled people need.

Should we stop at the integration of health and social care?

The aspiration to integrate the health and care systems is important. But could a whole person approach go further? Disabled people don't only fall between the cracks separating the health and social care system – but they must also navigate the welfare system, employment support and housing.

For example, many disabled people require social care support to seek and stay in employment. But employment support remains in a silo, simply focusing on building work-related skills and experience rather than ensuring people have a continuity of care that is a prerequisite to their working life. Ultimately if you can't get out of bed, get washed and get dressed, you will not be able to get to work in the morning.

Disabled people must navigate multiple assessment processes, meet a plethora of eligibility criteria only to have a number of different funding streams be devolved to them. Whole person care must understand the complexity of disabled people's interaction with the state and should be thought of alongside a disability support system that is simple to access and is itself based on the whole of the person.

A final thought

Finding a sustainable future for health and care is more urgent than ever. At a time when disabled people's costs of living are spiralling, and their income is flat-lining, they simply don't have the resources to continue to plug the gaps in the system. We must act fast if many more disabled people are not to be left in our communities without any support to do the basic in lives.

Whole person care could certainly be a big part of solving the current social care crisis for disabled people. There are certainly some big questions that remain unanswered, not least how a health system free at the point of access can be merged with a care system so dependent on eligibility and assessment. If these questions can be answered, Labour could be on the cusp of creating a care system fit for disabled people in the 21st century.

8 | TAKING THE WORKFORCE WITH YOU

Karen Jennings

Whole person care promises much for service users and staff alike. But health and social care staff have been subject to a huge number of recent reorganisations. For the policy to be a success it has to properly address the role of the workforce in delivering integration.

Integration has become the latest buzzword in public policy over the last few months, with the major political parties each bidding to outdo one another. There is an element of 'motherhood and apple pie' to this debate – after all, who wouldn't want services to be joined up better, with people receiving a more seamless experience of care, as responsibility is transferred from the NHS to local government or vice versa?

Matters have not been helped by the fact that the international comparisons are often wide of the mark. For example, the somewhat tired comparisons with the likes of Kaiser Permanente in the United States add little of use, with Kaiser integrating services within a hugely fragmented system of multiple providers – completely different from the starting point with the NHS.

Even some of the key proponents of integration, such as Jennifer Dixon at the Nuffield Trust, have pointed out that the evidence base for integration is "thin". The simple fact is that full national integration of health and social care has not been attempted in a country of comparable size or health demographics to England.

However, there is much to welcome in the idea of whole person care. As one would expect with plans of such ambition, there is also further work that needs to be done in order for the workforce to not merely be reassured about this new approach, but to be sufficiently enthused that they become advocates for it.

Markets versus integration

The government's belated conversion to integration has ironically come just as their wider market reforms are fragmenting the system, with new competition rules potentially blocking the likes of the Torbay Care Trust from continuing their much-lauded work.

Crucial to the success of whole person care is, therefore, recognition that the market can never deliver meaningful integration of services. The clumsy attempt to crowbar an integration remit into the role of competition enforcer Monitor demonstrates the incompatibility of the two.

It is essential that under whole person care, integration proceeds on the basis of NHS and public sector values, rather than permitting healthcare companies an easier route into provision simply by tacking a promise to work with social care services onto their bids.

So it is welcome that a starting point for whole person care is repeal of the Health and Social Care Act's regime of economic regulation. Similarly, plans to give the NHS the ability to reassert itself as the 'preferred provider' of healthcare are welcome.

For whole person care to raise the quality of social care provision, however, there would need to be a matching 'preferred provider' approach in social care, to break the downward spiral and arrest the alarming decline in quality of care that the current care market has produced.

Staff buy-in

Labour's policy has the potential to trump the others if it can properly address the role of health and care staff in delivering integration – something which is often absent from much of the wider narrative on integration, which seems to assume that a combination of altered structures and changed incentives will simply be imposed on those that work in delivering these services.

Those who deliver our public services are too readily dismissed as 'producer interest'. This is a myth that ignores the fact that these people are also on the receiving end of public services and so have a vested interest in producing high quality services for all.

It is encouraging therefore that the terms of reference of the Independent Commission on Whole Person Care include a need to outline the development needs of the workforce to achieve integrated care, and to test any recommendations with patients, users and practitioners, to ensure they are workable and effective.

The terms of reference also include moving to the new system "without major structural change and within existing resources". This looks challenging to say the least.

It may well be that by 2015 the current government will have made such a mess of the NHS and social care that it is impossible to avoid a major overhaul, but there needs to be consideration of how best to change the system while avoiding further unnecessary upheaval for staff and service users.

In common with other health and social care staff, Unison members have been subject to a huge number of recent reorganisations, particularly in the past two years with the commissioning changes in the NHS and with public health being transferred back to local government. As Andy Burnham has proposed, the onus on changing incentives, powers and cultures rather than structures might be one way of doing this, at least as a first step.

Funding and cuts

There would need to be a robust guarantee for citizens of the care they should expect to receive in the new system, given the lack of ring-fencing for NHS funds that would be transferred to local government. The inclusion for the first time of national standards for the delivery of social care within such an entitlement would be a very welcome move. The secretary of state would need powers to inter-vene in the event of any commissioners attempting to break away from delivering this national guarantee.

For whole person care to work, the system would need to be properly funded. There are currently major concerns about funding, particularly in social care where the Asso-ciation of Directors of Adult Social Services (ADASS) has warned recently that "a bleak outlook is getting bleaker".

It may well be that in the longer term, integration has the potential to save money by changing incentives and reducing duplication. But the fear amongst many health and care workers will be that the term 'integration' will simply be used as a cover for cuts (much in the way that personalisation has come to be associated with cuts in social care).

Raising up, not dragging down

There is therefore a need for reassurance that the positive intentions of whole person care cannot be twisted to justify cuts and dragging down to the lowest common denomina-tor. To this end, it is essential that whole person care aims to bring social care terms and conditions up, rather than pushing NHS terms and conditions down.

Labour should not ignore the possibility of 'two-tierism' developing in integrated workplaces, with one group of workers on one set of terms and conditions and another on a different set, working alongside each other in the same type of work. More broadly, cultural differences between different sets of workers need to be factored in and a new culture forged with the full involvement of staff. There is also a need to avoid the perception of a 'takeover' of one sector by the other.

The ultimate aim should be to move care workers into the NHS 'agenda for change' pay system. This would send out a very strong message that care work was no longer a minimum wage (or worse) occupation, but that those charged with looking after the most vulnerable would now be properly rewarded for the work they did.

In the shorter term, an expectation of national agenda for change pay arrangements could be written explicitly into the staff rights section of the NHS constitution. Any local infringement of this could then fall within the powers of the secretary of state to intervene in the event of a breach of the national care guarantee, which it is assumed the NHS constitution would form an important part of.

Ethical care, safe staffing

Whole person care could address unacceptable local authority commissioning practices by adopting the key components of Unison's 'ethical care charter'. This would ensure that local authorities only commission care which meets certain standards, including ending 15-minute visits, pay covering travel time to ensure fair wages, preventing short-changing of clients' allotted visit times, and ending the use of zero-hours contracts. The Office for National Statistics recently estimated that a shocking 200,000 people were on zero-hours contracts at the end of 2012.

Similarly, whole person care should guarantee safe minimum staffing levels in hospitals and other care settings to reduce the potential for harm, as recommended by the Francis report but ignored by the government. Legislation should be used to enshrine minimum staff-to-patient ratios in all healthcare settings, which would also provide peace of mind to families and healthcare staff.

There is growing evidence, from the UK and elsewhere, of the positive impact this can have, particularly in terms of lower patient mortality. The latest Unison survey of nursing members found that an alarming 45 per cent were looking after eight or more patients on their shift – the level at which research has demonstrated harm can be caused to patients.

Engaging the workforce

Whole person care is designed to work on the assumption that home rather than hospital should be the starting place for care. Unison has consistently supported the desire of service users to receive their care in the setting that is most appropriate for them, with care outcomes and overall wellbeing likely to be improved by receiving treatment in one's own home.

For this to become a reality, however, there would need to be a robust mechanism to allow staff currently working in acute hospital or care home settings more flexibility without fear of redundancy, cuts to terms and conditions, or infringements of staff wellbeing. Proper protocols that take note of important staffing issues – such as health and safety, education and training – would need to be drawn up if there is to be an expansion in the amount of home working or lone working undertaken by care staff.

This mirrors the need to engage as early as possible around wider reconfigurations of services, such as those designed to move more care into community settings. It is hardly surprising that attempts to change the delivery of services have met with such opposition from staff and communities, when plans have too often been sprung on local people with inadequate consultation or insufficient explanation of any clinical benefits.

Moving care from the hospital and into community settings should not become synonymous with privatisation; there is a need to ensure sufficient public sector capacity is built up in the community before such moves are attempted.

A national care service

Unison has long-established policy calling for a national care service in which social care is delivered on an NHS-style free at the point of need basis. With Labour holding out the prospect of an 'all-in' approach to social care funding as one of the options for moving to whole person care, this goal is tantalisingly within reach.

As society attempts to stretch resources to cover an ageing population, fear of getting older has never been greater. What better way for Labour to approach the next election than armed with a genuinely transformative policy to offer certainty and reassurance for when people reach old age?

Whole person care promises much for service users and staff alike. Inevitably there will be many details to be thrashed out and arguments to be had along the way.

But if Labour can successfully take the workforce with them, this has the potential to be not just a popular policy, but also one that changes the care landscape forever.

9 | THE PRINCIPLES OF FAIR ENTITLEMENTS

Michael Rawlins

Bringing together the disparate strands of entitlements in our current dysfunctional system will be a challenge. However there is a set of principles that can sustain a consensus in tough fiscal times and help guide the difficult decisions ahead.

At present, it seems a Utopian dream for comprehensive, whole person care – based on need – to be entirely funded by general taxation. The nation's current financial state would make this very challenging throughout the lifetime of the next administration and likely beyond that. Even if current budgets for health and social care remain protected – increasing, at best, only in line with inflation – the legitimate demands of increasing numbers of older people will outstrip current resources. Difficult – and sometimes unpopular – decisions will have to be made. This account is concerned exclusively with entitlements for adult whole person care and does not include entitlements for children and adolescents.

So what principles should underpin 'entitlements' to health and social care? And what will be the inevitable implications for individuals and their families?

First, the entitlements for both adult clinical and supportive care should be explicit and standardised across

England. Such entitlements should no longer be left to the idiosyncrasies of Clinical Commissioning Groups (CCGs) or local authorities. This will probably require the secretary of state to indicate, precisely, the clinical and support services to which people should be entitled.

Second, adults with long-term care needs should be entitled to a comprehensive assessment of their combined clinical and support service requirements. They should be entitled to advice on the available measures that will provide them with the opportunity to live as full and productive lives as circumstances permit.

Thirdly, people should be entitled to access clinical services that sustain health and prevent ill health and that are, as at present, largely free at the point of need.

Fourthly, people should be entitled to support services that sustain, as much as possible, their independence and the quality of their lives. Defined packages of clinical and supportive care should – in so far is as practical – enable them and their families to exercise choice.

Finally, if requirements exist for individuals to contribute to their clinical and support services, they should be fair and consistent across England. Fairness, in this context, refers to the provision of services consistent with commonly held views of social justice regarding priority being given to the most disadvantaged.

If these principles are accepted, there are implications for the provision of both clinical and support services, as well as for what are separate personal budgets for clinical and supportive care.

Clinical care

Patients are already required to contribute to some clinical services including, for example, aspects of dental and ophthalmological care. The clinical services to which all people should be entitled should encompass both clinical care in general practice (primary care) and in general district hospitals (secondary care) as well as in specialist hospitals (tertiary care).

1. Secondary and tertiary care.

Patients should be entitled to all in-patient care free of charge. Although it has been suggested that patients should be expected to pay for their 'hotel costs', I reject this as both inequitable as well as impractical. So-called 'hotel costs' might include the cost of hospital food but not much else. Cleaning and portering services, in hospitals, are intimately involved with the clinical environment. Moreover, the majority of patients are elderly and would either have to be exempted or subject to some sort of means test. The bureaucracy involved in the latter process, and taking account of the limited duration of stay of hospital inpatients (compared to supportive care in nursing homes), would make the whole process self-defeating.

As promised in the NHS Constitution, all patients should be entitled to those products that have been recommended by the National Institute for Health and Care Excellence (NICE). There have, in the past, been notable failures in meeting this explicit entitlement. So that the stain of 'postcode prescribing' is finally eradicated, the Care Quality Commission (CQC) should be required to confirm all Trusts' adherence to NICE technology appraisals guidance when they undertake their inspections.

Patients should not be entitled to complementary and alternative medicine techniques unless endorsed by NICE. Thus, while patients might be entitled to acupuncture for some forms of chronic backache (as indicated in the relevant NICE guideline) there should be no presumed entitlement to homeopathic treatments unless these have been specifically recommended by NICE.

2. Primary care.

Patients should continue to be entitled to consultations with the appropriate members of their primary care team free of charge. Although some have proposed consultation fees, there is clear evidence that user fees seriously prejudice the health of disadvantaged members of society.

Currently, prescriptions of medicines provided in primary care (as well as for prescriptions for hospital outpatients) attract a prescription charge of £7.85 per item. Nevertheless, there are so many exemptions that only about 40 per cent of prescriptions attract this charge. The devolved administrations in Wales and Scotland have abolished prescription charges and although it is tempting to propose a similar change to our arrangements in England, further work must be done on whether this is affordable.

In any case, the current arrangements for prescription charges require review in two respects. First, the range and extent of exemptions need to be examined in greater depth than that undertaken by Sir Ian Gilmore in his review in 2010 of prescription charges for people with so-called 'long-term conditions'. A re-examination should be based on the principle of fairness and that the most disadvantaged should be exempt from prescription charges. There should also be a radical review of the arrangements for the prescription of medical foods for those with specific dietary intolerance (eg coeliac disease). Such foods are prescribed by general practitioners and dispensed by community pharmacists. A review of what is appropriate for the health service to provide, by way of medical foods, and how best to support those affected, should also be accompanied by a critical examination of whether medical food products could not be more economically dispensed by grocery stores rather than pharmacists.

As with entitlements in secondary care, only those complementary and alternative medicines, specifically approved by NICE, should be available in primary care.

Adult supportive care

Adult supportive care provides people, particularly the elderly, with help to live in dignity at home or, for those with greater needs, in residential care. Public expenditure on personal social services in 2011–2012, however, amounted to just over £15 billion, and would have been substantially greater if individuals had not themselves contributed to their care. The current arrangements, as clearly stated in the Dilnot report, are in urgent need of reform. As the report put it:

> *"Having to cope with a care and support need – both emotionally and financially – often comes as a major shock. When people then experience the system, many perceive it to be unfair. This is particularly the case when people have to sell their homes, or use up the majority of any assets they have, to pay for care. The current system does not encourage or reward saving, and is poorly understood. People are not prepared, which often leads to poor outcomes and considerable distress."*

Entitlements to supportive care should mainly follow the recommendations of the Dilnot report. First, people who enter adulthood already having a care need, should be entitled to the provision of full supportive care with no expectation of making any contribution to their care and with no means test. Such individuals will have had no opportunity to make provision for their care and, on grounds of fairness, it would be wrong to expect them to contribute to their supportive care needs.

Second, people in residential care are entitled to be well-nourished and provided with appropriate assistance for normal daily living. Unlike hospital inpatients, however, their needs are long-term; and their environments are domestic rather than clinical. Moreover, had they continued to live at home they would have had to pay for their own living costs. It is therefore fair that they should make an appropriate contribution to the costs of residential care. In the Dilnot report it was suggested that such contributions should amount to £7,000 to £10,000 per annum although I think that this is probably too high.

Third, once an individual's total contributions to their supportive care costs reach a threshold, they should be entitled to full support from public funds. The Dilnot report suggested that this threshold be put at between £25,000 and £50,000 and the government have recently proposed a cap of £72,000. It is, indeed, fair that some cap be placed on the lifetime contributions that individuals make to their care. The exact amount will inevitably depend on the UK's financial position at the time whole person care is introduced.

Fourthly, individuals in residential care with assets (including housing assets) of less than £14,500 are only expected to contribute to their care from their income. For those with assets in excess of £23,500, the current arrangements provide no financial support for their care. This is unfair and provides no incentive for individuals, at an earlier phase of their lives, to provide for their own future. The Dilnot report proposed that this so-called asset cap be increased from £23,250 to £100,000, and the government has set it at £118,000. It could be asked whether a cap at this higher level is affordable, but fairness demands that it be increased over and above current levels.

Personal whole person care budgets

As from April 2013, individuals receiving help from social services can now have a personal budget. This provides them with options as to how their needs are met and funded, as well as the support needed to make informed choices. It is intended to ensure that the services individuals receive meet their particular needs and wishes. From April 2014, individuals with continuing long-term health-care needs will be entitled to personal healthcare budgets.

Where successful, such personal budgets are popular with patients, their carers and their families as well as with patient advocacy groups. However, it makes no sense in an environment of whole person care to continue with separate clinical and support care budgets. Although merging them into a single whole person care budget offers challenges, plans should start to be made now. Entitlements within these combined personal care budgets should though be confined to those elements that are cost effective. Advice should be sought from NICE about the appropriate elements that should be contained within these packages and would exclude, for example, those complementary and alternative medicines that the Institute has advised as cost ineffective in the circumstances for which they would be used.

Conclusion

Determining entitlements for whole person care under the existing fragmented system will be untidy, especially in the early years. No one designing a health and care system today would devise a scheme resembling anything approaching our current dysfunctional arrangements. Each has evolved with its own sets of entitlements, and knitting these together will be challenging. The difficulties should not, though, dissuade us from making a start based on solid principles upon which reasonable people can agree.

10 | THE CHANGING ROLE OF THE GENERAL PRACTITIONER
Clare Gerada

The patients of tomorrow will be increasingly complex, and the twin scourges of poor continuity of care and increasing fragmentation of care need to be addressed. The GP's role will increasingly become one of the patient advocate and navigator – helping to co-ordinate their patient's care across an increasingly complicated provider network.

A ndy Burnham's ambitious and timely speech at the King's Fund, which introduced the idea of whole person care, focused on the vital issue of integration around the patient – bringing health and social care more aligned around the needs of the patient. This approach should be welcomed and I hope other political parties follow suit in identifying and acting on this important issue.

Integration is vital as we move forward to address the problems caused by poor continuity of care and fragmentation. Patients have multiple needs that require more than 'health' and are not best served by competition but instead collaboration between health (physical and mental) services, local government, housing, education and others.

General practice has always been a cornerstone of the NHS and will continue to be essential in the NHS of tomorrow; whatever system emerges there will always be a need for a generalist practitioner, able to deal with un-differentiated symptoms and act as a bridge to the rest of the health and social care system.

Even today, but more so in the future, the GP keeps the NHS safe, fair and offering value for money. Data shows that already over 1 million people are seen each day in general practice, who carry out 90 per cent of all activity for as little as 9 per cent of the NHS budget. General practitioners refer around one in 20 patients to a specialist, meaning that the vast majority of a patient's care is carried out by the GP and GP nurses.

GPs have always adapted to change and are skilled at creating solutions to problems that arise and will continue to deliver high quality but low-cost primary care; making the best use of the time and resources available to them to reduce health inequality throughout the UK; use IT effectively in delivering care; and become leaders in research and development.

There are problems, however, with the current system of general practice which will have to be addressed if GPs, in the future, are to be able to deliver the care that is required for their patients. The patients of tomorrow will be increasingly complex, and have many more 'comorbidities' (for example, a single patient may have diabetes, hypertension, heart disease, depression, osteoporosis and many more long-term problems). Many of our patients will have dementia and many will lead isolated lives. The problems that therefore need to be addressed, which are not unique to the UK (and paradoxically which, because of our GP system of care, we are best able to deal with), are the twin scourges of poor continuity of care and increasing fragmentation of care. Both of these increase costs, as patients are passed from one specialist to another, or from health to social care providers and in doing so, risk duplication of effort and poor patient outcomes. GPs are ideally placed to deal with patients with complex problems. But given the paucity of investment in the profession and the increased move of care outside hospitals, GPs are heaving under the workload, coupled with the decreased number of doctors entering the profession. Real investment – through redistribution of current resources (moving monies and people from hospitals to the community) – is required to create the capacity for GPs to undertake the work necessary to deliver a sustainable health service.

Together with investment, GPs will need to change the ways they work. To start, the concept of a fixed 10-minute GP-patient consultation is outdated and does not allow us to focus on the complex needs of our patients or to deliver the care we need to keep them safe in the community for as long as possible.

Consultations in the future will need to be flexible in duration depending on individual patient needs. They must offer flexibility in the location of consultations to incorporate home visits and there will be fewer each day, in order to offer longer consultations.

As set out in the the Royal College of General Practitioners' (RCGP) future vision for general practice, *The 2022 GP*, general practice will also move beyond face-to-face appointments. Patients will be encouraged to remotely 'visit' their GP by telephone, email, text message and through social media. This has the potential to extend to virtual examinations by doctors and practice nurses in settings outside the confines of the surgery and at more flexible times.

GPs in 2022 will promote self-care by referring patients to e-health information systems. Shared decision-making between GPs, patients and carers will also become the norm.

In addition, patients will have remote interaction with their GP, with the ability to move directly from registration to treatment, as well as online access to their medical records, an innovation that is already in motion.

Given more GPs, we will be able to deliver better integrated care – joined-up care where different professionals come together around the needs of the patient, rather than expecting the patient to travel across multiple providers. Integrated care in this context is GP led multi-professional teams, working together with communication that goes beyond the simple exchange of letters, with the different professionals working across their professional boundaries (so in and out of hospital, in and out of 'core' hours), ideally with pooled budgets and ideally with shared GP electronic records. Patients identified as high risk of hospital admission (for example, the frail elderly) or those at the end of their lives are best suited to an integrated approach, which should include better-personalised care during the 24-hour period. This does not mean the GP returning to 24-hour responsibility for all patients, but sharing the care of patients to help improve their lives and reduce unnecessary hospital admission.

General practitioners in the UK do more for more patients, and to a greater level of complexity, than many GPs across the world. Yet we have one the shortest training programmes. Three year compulsory vocational training was introduced in the UK 30 years ago, yet a UK GP now delivers care that would have been the territory of a consultant physician, or psychiatrist or public health doctor. In 2012 the RCGP obtained educational approval for enhanced GP training – meaning that, once ministerial go ahead for implementation is given, the GP of the future will have enhanced and extended training, with all new trainees completing a four-year training programme.

GPs will continue to be experts in generalism but enhanced training will equip them with the skills to: co-ordinate cost-effective care for patients with multiple-morbidities and individual conditions; effectively manage complex and chronic medical conditions as well as end-of-life care; deal with polypharmacy (use of multiple medicines); understand the health needs of the community; and lead care in nursing homes and take care of the homeless and those with mental illness.

Extended training will include specific clinical training, focussing on paediatrics, care of the elderly, mental health and alcohol and substance misuse. GPs in 2022 will also acquire leadership skills to become leaders in education, training and research and in planning services and public health.

To meet the challenges facing general practice, there needs to be adaptation of the practice and the teams in which GPs work. Increasing numbers of the future work force are women working part time. However, far from being a disadvantage, given the complexity of our clinical work, part-time working is perhaps the best way of ensuring that patients continue to receive care from an empathetic and alert GP. However, we will have to learn to deliver continuity of care while adapting the ways we work to accommodate the changing demographics of our workforce, for example through job sharing, buddying systems or other organisational changes.

The 2022 GP sees practice nurses and staff completing vocational training in primary care in order to help patients understand their illnesses. Practice teams will also include practitioners with specialist knowledge, skills and experience in order to effectively integrate care.

Communities will contain GP practice federations, working together to provide extended primary care services, including nursing and other community care programmes, such as dietary workshops.

The role of GP as gatekeeper will diminish as more services are provided directly and with self-referral possibilities for patients. However, the GP will continue to work towards less fragmented care, working with specialists and private, NHS and third sector health-care providers. The GP's role will increasingly become one of the patient advocate and navigator – helping to coordinate their patient's care across an increasingly complicated provider network.

What must not change is the relationship between the GP and their community, and through this the registered list. Removing GP boundaries by allowing patients to register with any GP, anywhere, will destroy this relationship and will widen health inequalities risking the creation of 'sink practices'. GPs must care for patients within the context of their families and communities – and a geographical boundary and registered population is the way of doing this.

The future is bright for general practice but in order for *The 2022 GP* to become a reality we need to attract more graduates to enter general practice and retain the existing workforce, offering all GPs opportunities for high quality training and employment. Despite the pressures that the NHS is under today – and will no doubt be in the future – only by investing in primary, community and social care can we hope to deliver a health care system fit for the future.

A VISION OF WHOLE PERSON
CARE FOR A 21ST CENTURY
HEALTH AND CARE SERVICE

EDITED BY
ANDY BURNHAM MP

FABIAN
SOCIETY

Discussion Guide: Together

How to use this Discussion Guide

The guide can be used in various ways by Fabian Local Societies, local political party meetings and trade union branches, student societies, NGOs and other groups.

- You might hold a discussion among local members or invite a guest speaker – for example, an MP, academic or local practitioner to lead a group discussion.

- Some different key themes are suggested. You might choose to spend 15–20 minutes on each area, or decide to focus the whole discussion on one of the issues for a more detailed discussion.

A discussion could address some or all of the following questions:

1. Andy Burnham said in his speech to the King's Fund, which introduced the whole person care concept, that it would "give local government a positive future and local communities a real say…It won't be the job of people at local level to decide what should be provided. That will be set out in a new entitlement. But it will be their job to decide how it should be provided. That would provide clarity about the respective roles of national and local government, too often a source of confusion and tension." What is needed to get the most out of this relationship between the central and the local, for whole person care? Can the centre genuinely let go, whilst still maintain a strong role in creating institutions and setting policy goals?

2. In a recent Fabian interview, Andy Burnham rued the fact that, when it comes to older people, hospitals "are not geared to deal with all their needs." But more and more, hospitals are where older people end up, rather than being given the support they need to stay independent in their own homes. Hospital CEOs report that, on any given day, around 30 to 40 per cent of beds are occupied by older people who, if better provision was available, would not need to be there. Does the one-budget, one-person world offer the possibility of keeping older people at home and out of hospital?

Please let us know what you think

Whatever view you take of the issues, we would very much like to hear about your discussion. Please send us a summary of your debate (perhaps 300 words) to debate@fabians.org.uk.

JOIN
BRITAIN'S ONLY
MEMBERSHIP
THINK TANK

Members of the Fabian Society receive
at least four pamphlets or books a year as
well as our quarterly magazine, 'Fabian
Review'. You'll also receive invitations to
special members' events and regular
lectures and debates with leading
politicians and thinkers.

For just £3 a month you can join now and
we'll send you two pamphlets and the latest
magazine free.

Call 020 7227 4900, email us at
info@fabian-society.org.uk, or go to
www.fabians.org.uk for more information

The Shape of Things to Come

Labour's New Thinking

After the 1970s it was inevitable that the Conservative party would move away from the postwar consensus, but it was Margaret Thatcher who made it Thatcherite. In the 1990s Labour was bound to be centrist; but Blair and Brown gave New Labour its distinctive shape.

After the banking crisis Labour was bound to reflect a public mood more critical of neo-liberal economics, and less confident about big state spending, but Labour in 2012 will also be shaped by the particular politics and personality of Ed Miliband.

Since becoming Labour leader Ed Miliband has successfully opened several new national political debates, from the 'squeezed middle' to 'responsible capitalism' and concern about diminishing opportunities for the rising generation.

These essays explore where this politics could take Labour – and there is a striking coherence, radicalism and optimism about the future they see.